Play piano for wel

FABER *ff* MUSIC

© 2020 by Faber Music Ltd.
First published in 2020 by Faber Music Ltd.
Bloomsbury House
74–77 Great Russell Street
London WC1B 3DA

Cover design by Adam Hay Studio
Cover image by Chakkree Chantakad
Music arranged by Oliver Weeks and Lucy Holliday
Edited by Lucy Holliday

Printed and bound in the UK by Caligraving Ltd
All rights reserved

ISBN: 0-571-54177-1
EAN: 978-0-571-54177-5

To buy Faber Music publications or to find out about the full range of titles available
please contact your local retailer or Faber Music sales enquiries:

Faber Music Limited, Burnt Mill, Elizabeth Way, Harlow, CM20 2HX, England
Tel: +44 (0) 1279 82 89 82
fabermusic.com

A Catalogue Of Afternoons

Composed by Max Richter

Both Sides Now

Words and Music by Joni Mitchell

1. Rows and floes of an-gel hair and ice - cream cas - tles in the air,___ and
2. Moons and Junes and Fer - ris wheels, the diz - zy danc - ing way you feel___ as
3. Tears and fears and feel-ing proud, to say, "I love you" right out loud,

fea - ther can - yons___ ev-'ry - where, I've looked at clouds that way.
ev - 'ry fair - y___ tale comes real, I've looked at love that way.
dreams and schemes and___ cir-cus crowds, I've looked at life that way.

But now they on - ly block the sun___ they rain and snow___ on ev-'ry - one___ so
But now it's just an - o-ther show,___ you leave 'em laugh - ing when you go,___ and
But now old friends are act-ing strange, they shake their heads, they say I've changed, well

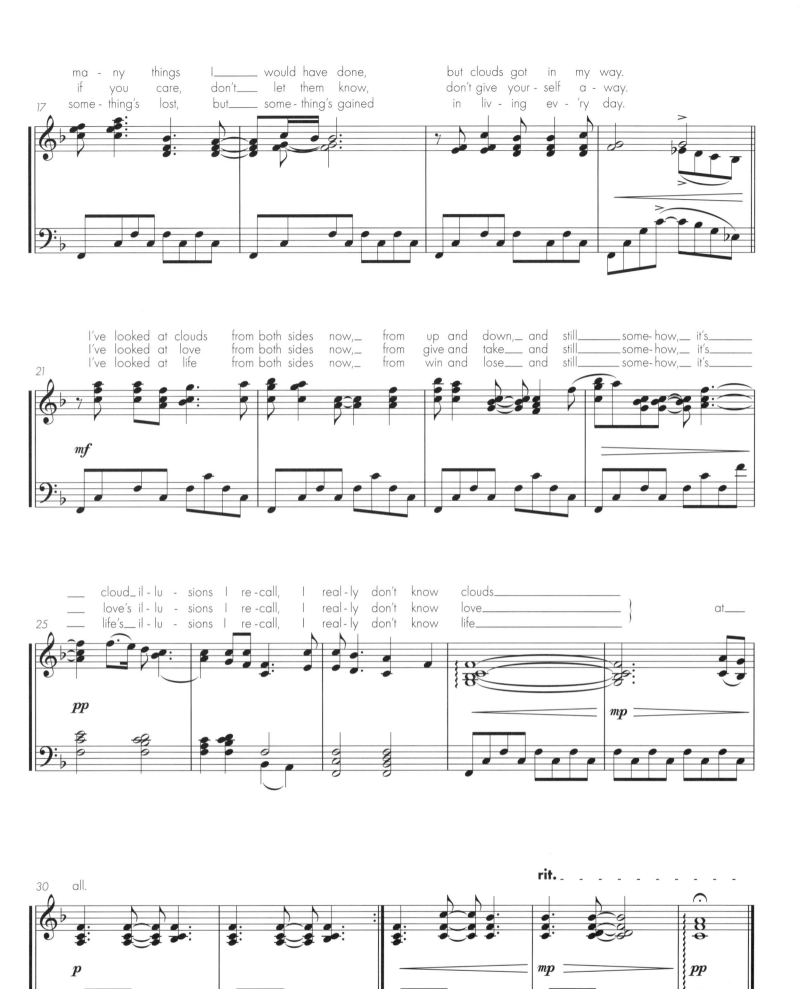

ma - ny things I_____ would have done, but clouds got in my way.
if you care, don't_____ let them know, don't give your - self a - way.
some - thing's lost, but_____ some - thing's gained in liv - ing ev - 'ry day.

I've looked at clouds from both sides now,_ from up and down,_ and still_____some-how,_ it's_____
I've looked at love from both sides now,_ from give and take__ and still_____some-how,_ it's_____
I've looked at life from both sides now,_ from win and lose__ and still_____some-how,_ it's_____

___ cloud_ il - lu - sions I re-call, I real - ly don't know clouds_____
___ love's il - lu - sions I re-call, I real - ly don't know love_____ } at___
___ life's_ il - lu - sions I re-call, I real - ly don't know life_____

all.

rit. _ _ _ _ _ _ _ _ _ _ _ _

Danny Boy

Traditional

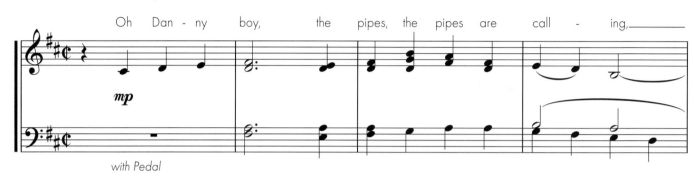

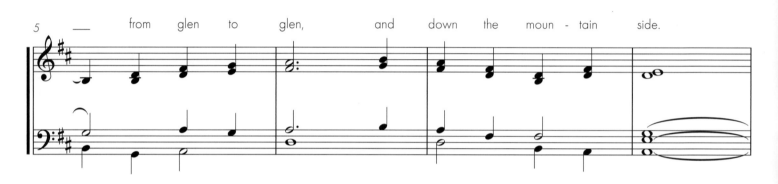

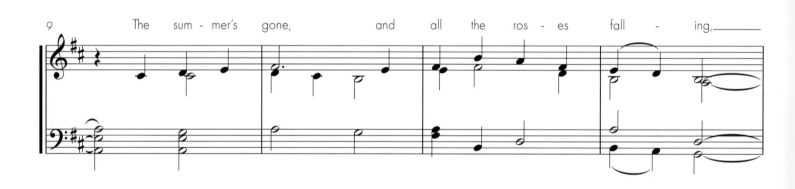

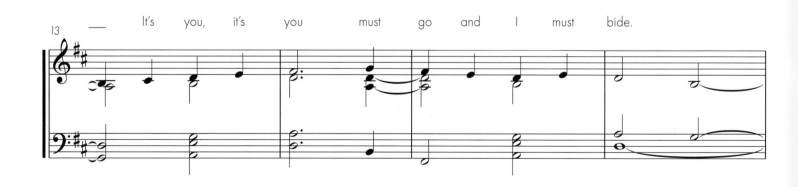

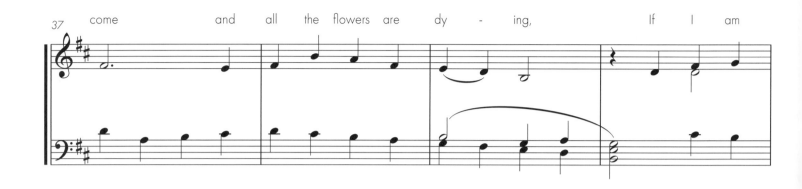

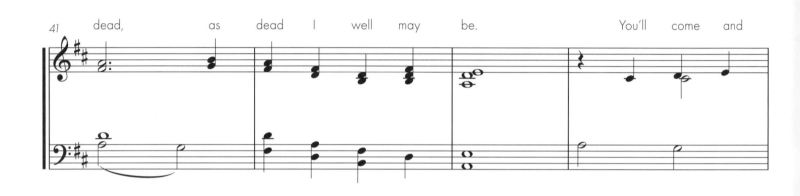

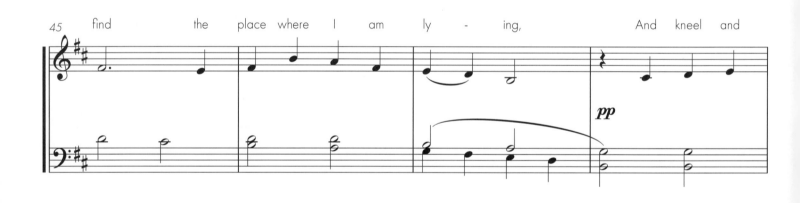

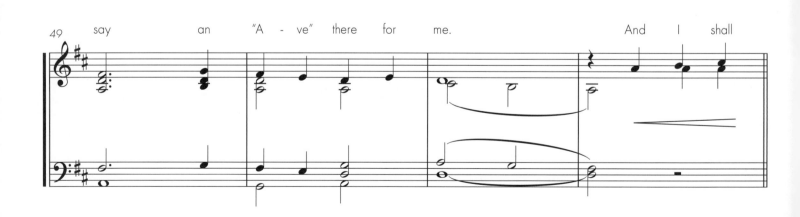

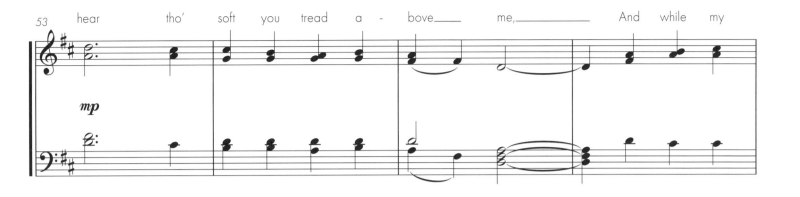

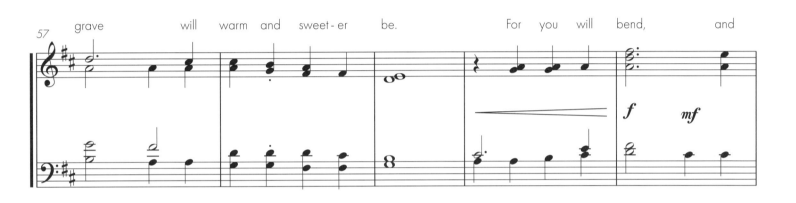

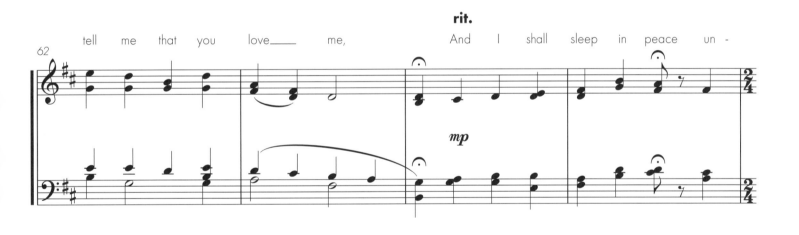

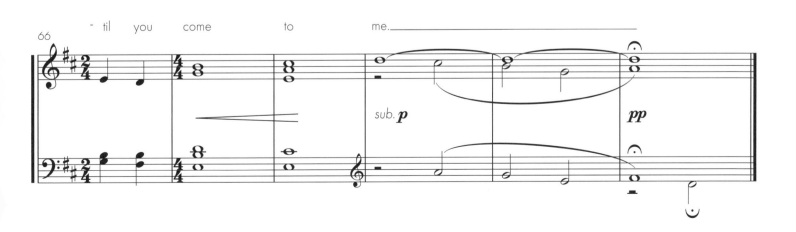

Embraceable You

Music and Lyrics by George Gershwin and Ira Gershwin

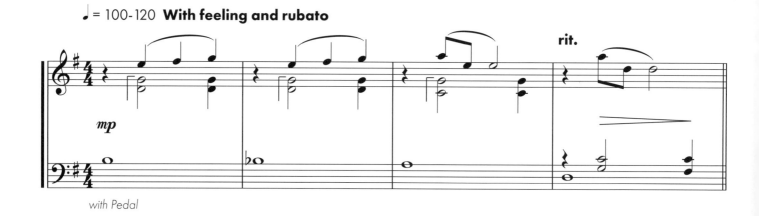

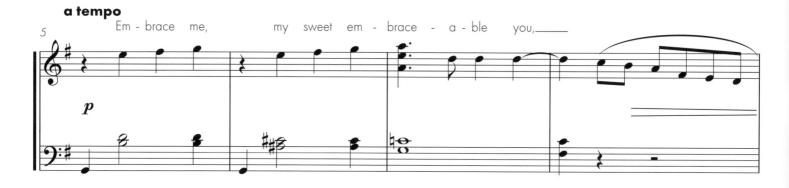

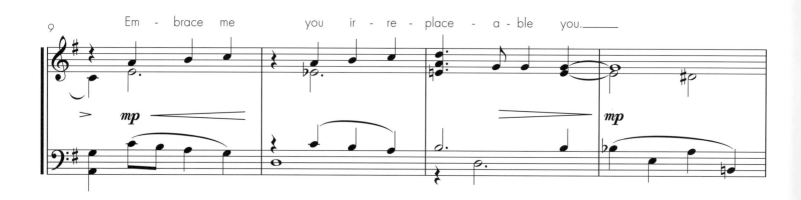

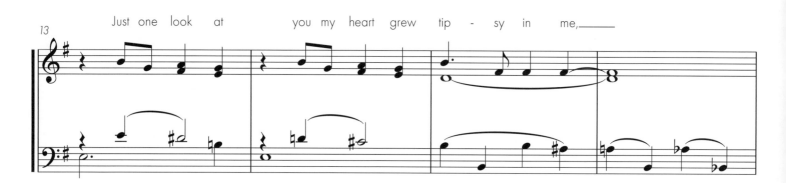

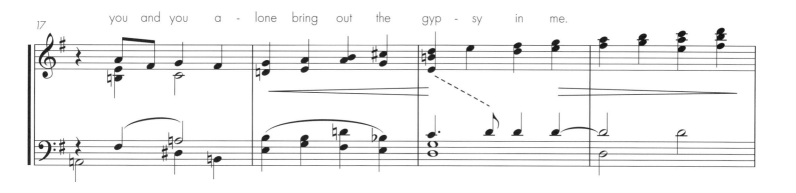

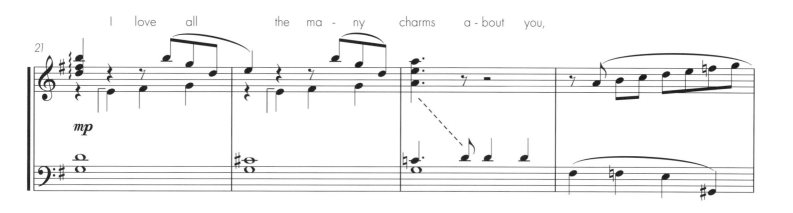

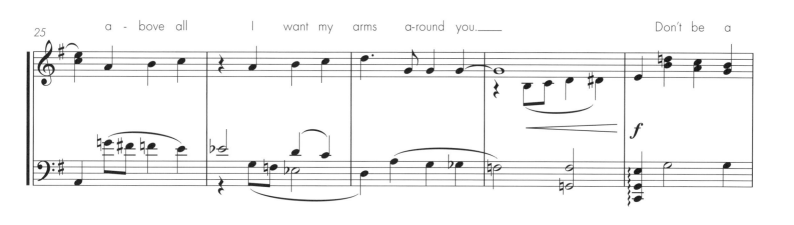

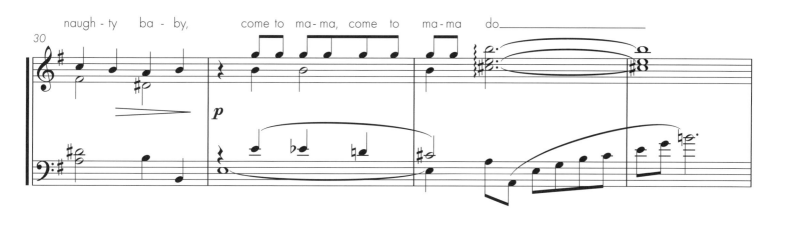

my sweet em - brace - a - ble you.

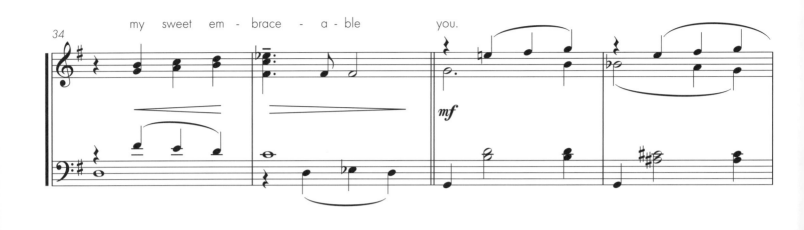

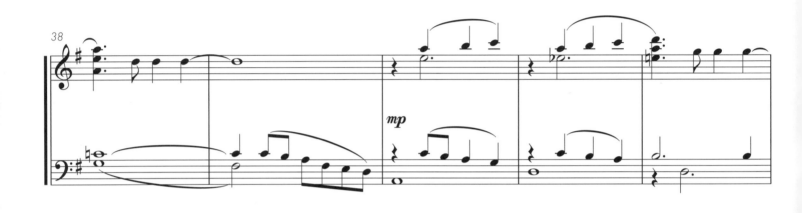

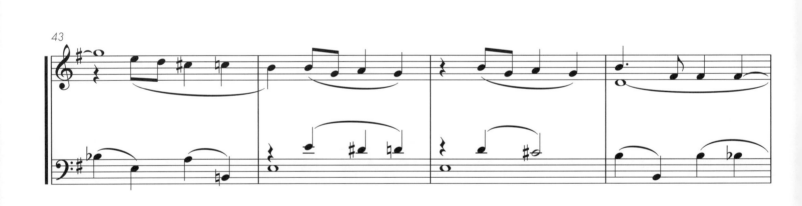

The Glory Of Love

Words and Music by Billy Hill

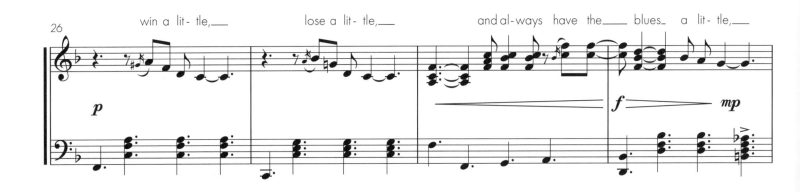

win a lit- tle,___   lose a lit- tle,___   and al-ways have the___ blues___ a lit- tle,___

1.

that's the sto- ry of,___   that's the glo- ry___ of love.

2.

that's the glo- ry___ of love,

Freely   **rit.** _ _ _ _ _ _ _ _ _ _ _

that's the sto- ry of,___   that's the glo- ry of love.

18

Gymnopédie No. 1 (from *Trois Gymnopédies*)

Composed by Erik Satie

20

21

Gottes Zeit ist die allerbeste Zeit
(Actus Tragicus) BWV 106

Composed by Johann Sebastian Bach

(Small notes optional)

Heroes

Words by David Bowie
Music by David Bowie and Brian Eno

Havana

Words and Music by Louis Bell, Brian Lee, Jeffery Williams, Adam Feeney, Pharrell Williams,
Ali Tamposi, Camila Cabello, Brittany Hazzard, Andrew Wotman, Andrew Watt and Brandon Perry

This is history in the makin' homie (homie)

she waited on me (and what?)   *Shawty cakin' on me, got the bacon on me (wait up)*

Point blank, close range, that B   *if it cost a million, that's me (that's me)*   *I was gettin' mula, baby...   Ha -*

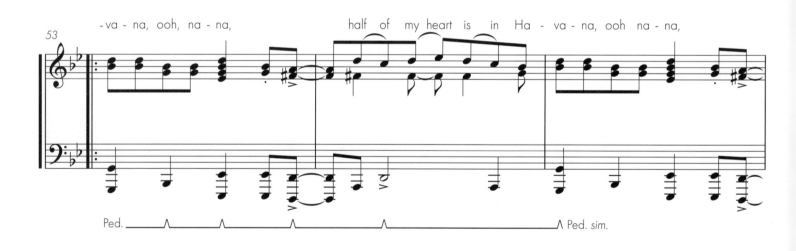

-va - na, ooh, na - na,   *half of my heart is in Ha - va - na, ooh na - na,*

Ped. ___ ∧ ___ ∧ ___ ∧ ___ ∧ ___ ∧ Ped. *sim.*

he took me back to East At - lan - ta, na - na - na,   *oh but my heart is in Ha-*

I Giorni

Composed by Ludovico Einaudi

I Vow To Thee, My Country

Composed by Gustav Holst

Largo (from *New World Symphony*)

Composed by Antonín Dvořák

Let There Be Love

Words and Music by Ian Grant and Lionel Rand

41

The Lord Is My Shepherd (Psalm 23)

Composed by Howard Goodall

Lovely Day

Words and Music by Skip Scarborough and Bill Withers

46

Lost

Words and Music by Frank Ocean, James Ho, Paul Shelton II and Micah Otano

♩ = 125 **Wistful**

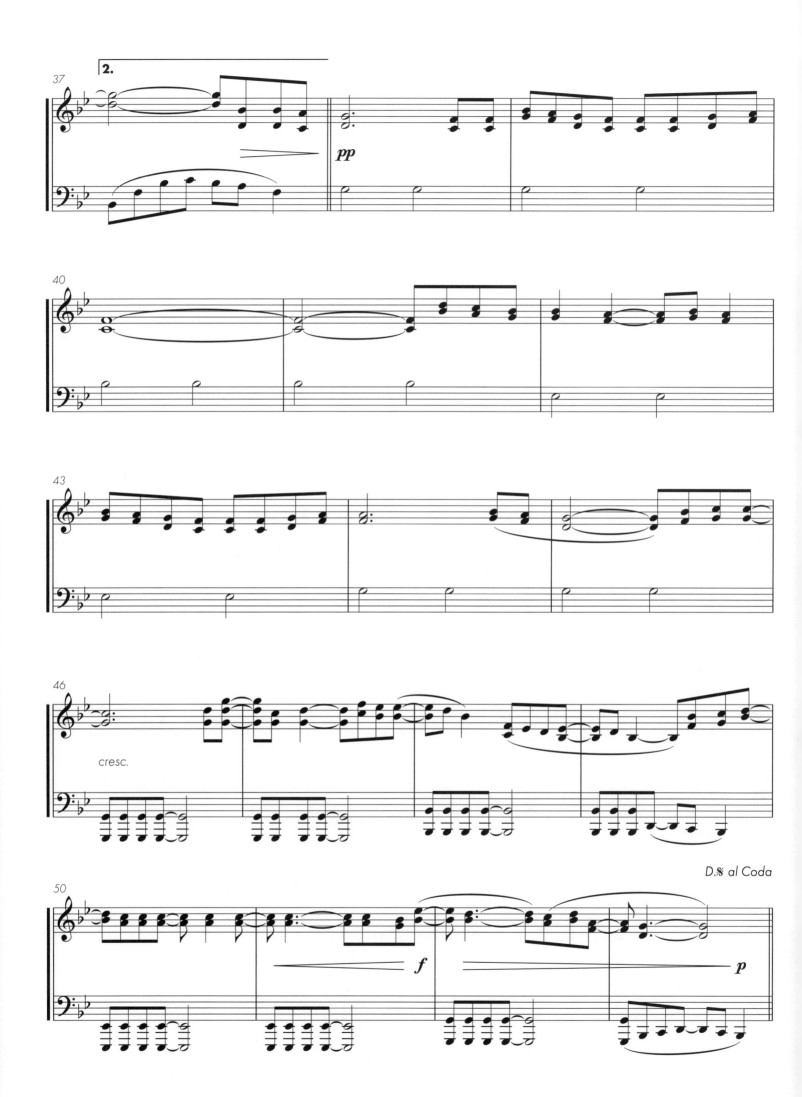

D.𝄉 al Coda

Coda

Mia & Sebastian's Theme

Composed by Justin Hurwitz

As fast as possible, freely

Morning (from *Peer Gynt Suite*)

Composed by Edvard Grieg

Moonlight Sonata, Op.27, No.2
(Abridged)

Composed by Ludwig van Beethoven

Adagio sostenuto

pp legato

con Ped.

Nimrod (from *Enigma Variations* Op.36)

Composed by Edward Elgar

No Surprises

Words and Music by Thomas Yorke, Jonathan Greenwood,
Colin Greenwood, Edward O'Brien and Philip Selway

64

Over The Rainbow (from *The Wizard Of Oz*)

Music by Harold Arlen
Lyrics by E.Y. "Yip" Harburg

67

River Flows In You

By Yiruma

The Parting Glass

Traditional

73

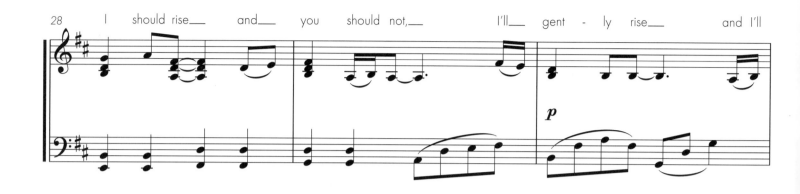

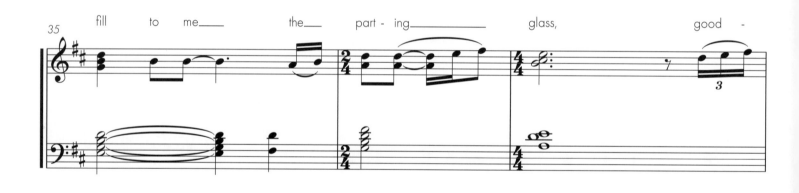

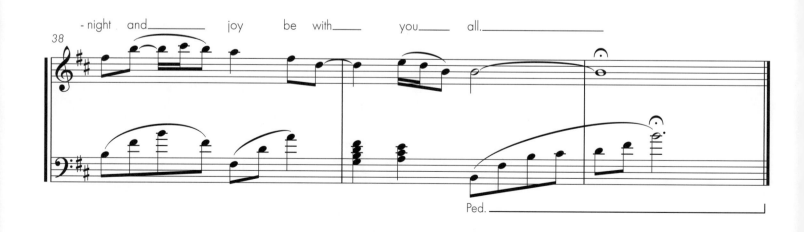

A Sky Full Of Stars

Words and Music by Guy Berryman, Jon Buckland,
Will Champion, Chris Martin and Tim Bergling

76

'Cause in a sky_____ 'cause in a sky_____ full of stars_____ I think I { saw } { see }

you.

To Coda ⊕

mf

f

D. % al Coda

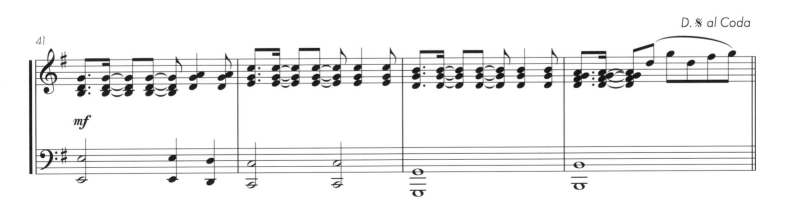

mf

77

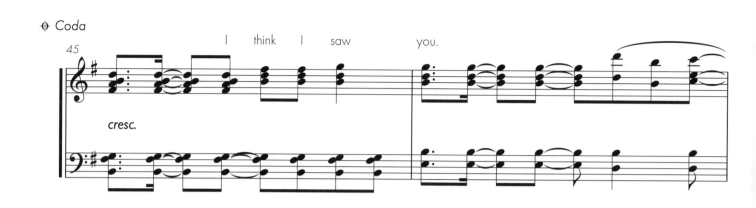

I think I saw you.

You're a sky_____ you're a sky_____ full of stars,___ such a hea-ven-ly

view...   Such a hea-ven-ly

view...

mp

79

Sleeping Lotus

Composed by Joep Beving

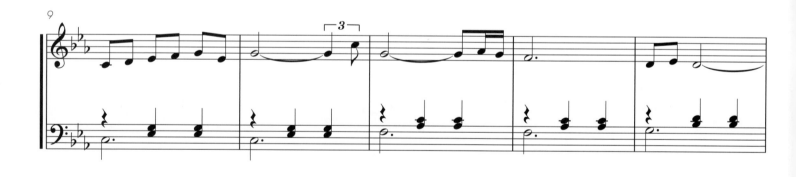

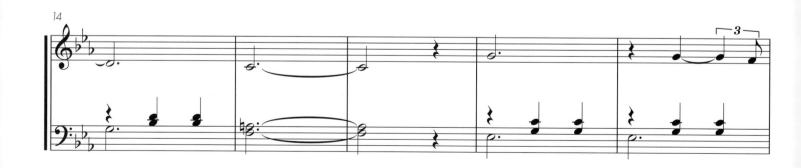

Sweet Caroline

Words and Music by Neil Diamond

1. Where it be - gan,___ I can't be - gin to know - in'
(2.) look at the night___ and it don't seem so lone - ly,

but then I know___ it's grow - ing strong._____
we fill it up___ with on - ly two._____

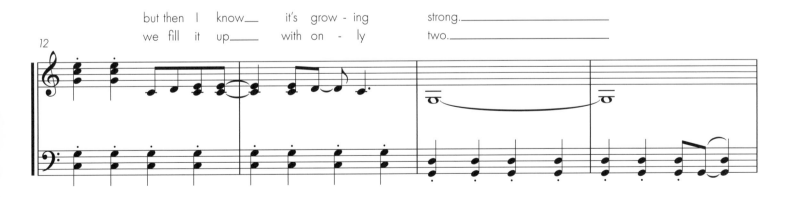

Someone To Watch Over Me

Music and Lyrics by George Gershwin and Ira Gershwin

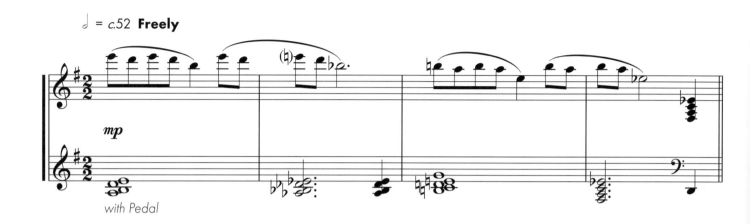

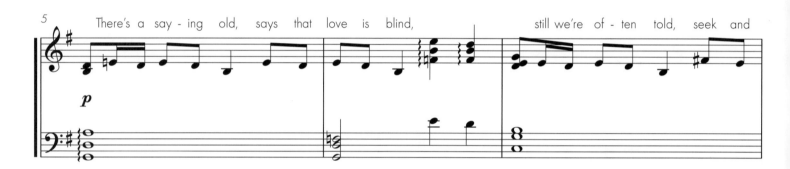

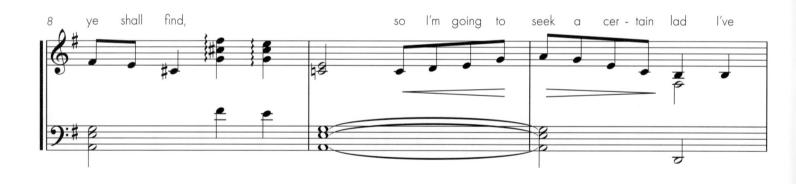

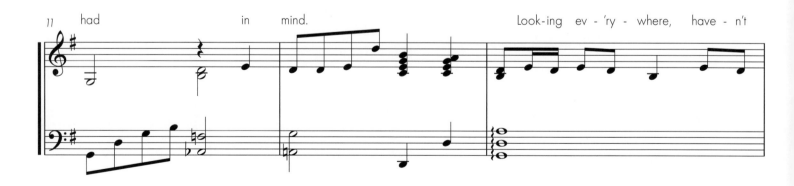

14 found him yet, he's the big af - fair I can - not for - get,

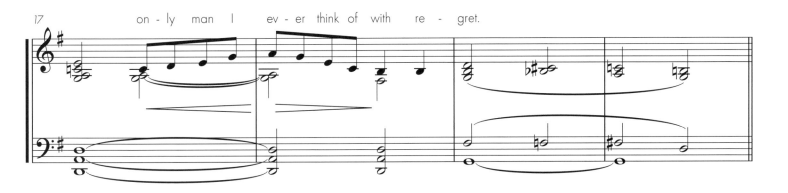

17 on - ly man I ev - er think of with re - gret.

21 I'd like to add his in - i - tials to my mon - o - gram.

mf

rit.

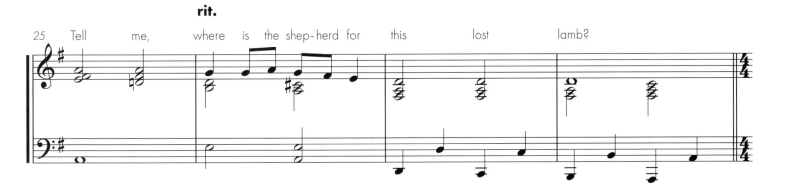

25 Tell me, where is the shep - herd for this lost lamb?

Slowly, in time

29 There's a some - bo - dy I'm long - ing to see. I hope that he___ 3

mp

90

In tempo

Won't you tell him please to put on some speed, fol - low my lead, oh, how_ I need some-one to watch ov-er me; some-one to watch ov-er me.

Slowly

What A Wonderful World

Words and Music by George Weiss and Bob Thiele

The White Cliffs Of Dover

Words and Music by Walter Kent and Nat Burton

You Can't Always Get What You Want

Words and Music by Mick Jagger and Keith Richards

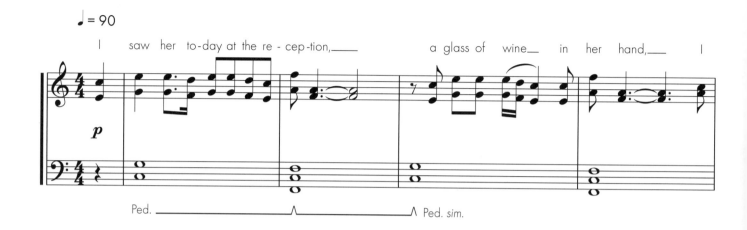

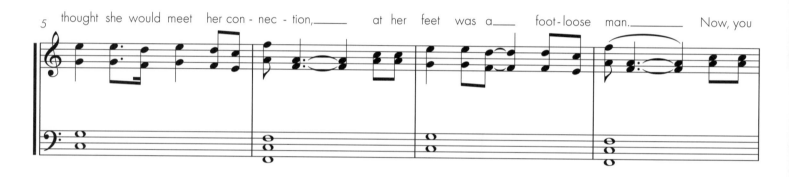

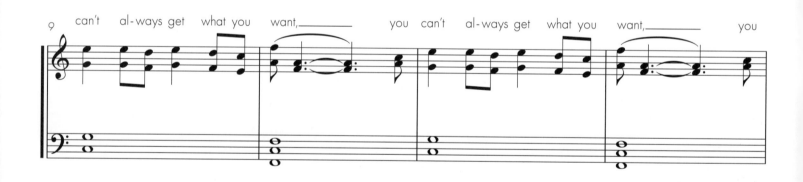

need.

simile

%

1. I	saw her to-day at the re - cep - tion,	
(2.)	went down to the de - mon - stra-tion,	to get
(3.)	down to the Chel-sea drug - store,	to get
%.	saw her to-day_ at the re - cep - tion,	In her glass_

1°, %. *p*
2°, 3° *mp*

a glass of wine in her hand,_   I   knew she was gon-na meet her con - nec-
my fair share of a - buse._   Singing:_ "We're   gon-na vent our frus-tra -
your pre - scrip-tion filled,_   I was standin' in line   with Mis-ter Jim -
was a bleed - ing man,_   she was prac - tised_ at the art   of de-cep-

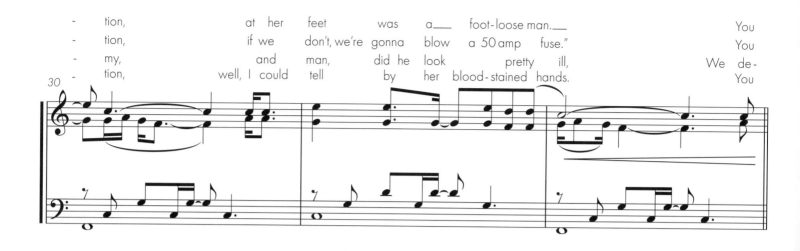

101